C000221818

The Spoons Murder

and other mysteries

The Spoons Murder

and other mysteries

Con Ó Drisceoil

Illustrated by Édain O'Donnell

Craft Recordings : Dublin 2006

Published 2006 by
CRAFT RECORDINGS
71 Bluebell Road, Dublin 12
Telephone 00 353 1 4299811

0 9553112 0 9
978 0 9553112 0 8

Music settings & layout - Terry Moylan

CONTENTS

Introduction

When I try to recall my earliest memories of songs, I first think of my mother, who taught us songs in Irish and in English, at home and in school, and who was definitely the musical parent; we never heard a note of song from my father. But when I think of comic songs, I know that my father certainly had a taste for them. When the Pye electric record-player arrived in our house to great excitement some time in the mid-sixties, the first LP he bought was Brendan O'Dowda's record of Percy French songs. Shortly after that came some Gilbert and Sullivan records: I remember being taken to see an amateur production of *HMS Pinafore* in Skibbereen Town Hall, and I wore out the *Pinafore* record in the ensuing months. I also have vivid memories of hearing "I am the Very

Model of a Modern Major-General", from *The Pirates of Penzance,* on the radio and being fascinated by the outrageous rhymes and by the way in which the listener is teased and taunted into trying to guess the next rhyme.

When I got to hear the Beatles and the Rolling Stones, of course, all that stuff was hastily disowned, and Lennon and McCartney became the new song-writing gods, with their apparently endless stream of brilliant songs. They also had a sense of humour that was subtle, whimsical and ironic, but it was the melodies and the arrangements that first appealed to me in this case.

Traditional songs gradually became a serious interest when I started to spend lots of time in the Gaeltacht area of Corca Dhuibhne throughout the seventies; my appetite for this music had been whetted by listening to Seán Ó Riada's thoughts on sean-nós during the last years of his life. I was lucky enough to know some fine singers in those years, people such as Seán de hÓra and Muiris Ó Dálaigh, and in my naiveté I even tried to imitate them. While some of their songs were light-hearted, I can't recall many comic songs featuring regularly in the repertoire of that area, compared to that of Conamara or Múscraí.

It was Múscraí that was to provide me with comic inspiration, mainly through my acquaintance with Diarmuidín Ó Súilleabháin during his years in Cork city. Those of us who played and heard music in the Phoenix bar in the seventies and early eighties had a habit of spending nights or weekends in Cúil Aodha and Baile Mhúirne, where we were all fascinated by the songs of Dónall Ó Mulláin, George Curtin, Patsy Cronin and others; and we could also hear newly arrived residents such as Deaglán Tallon picking up the tradition and producing amusing songs on current events. Among our own number, Jimmy Crowley was the bard, penning songs on the price of the pint, the introduction of the breathalyser, and other issues that seemed mightily relevant to us at the time. My introduction to "The Pool Song" in this volume tells the story from that point on: it struck me that I wanted to have a go, and there it started.

As your songs become more widely known and sung, the stimulus of meeting and hearing like-minded people encourages you. In recent years, since I began to make a more conscious effort to produce songs on a regular basis, I've got to hear more comic songs and to meet more songwriters: Seán Mone, Brian Ó Ruairc, Tim Lyons, Fintan Vallely, Mícheál Marrinan and many more. Writers I haven't met, such as Adam McNaughtan from Glasgow, become an influence. With increased confidence comes a desire to tackle subjects or challenges I wouldn't have dreamed of previously; twenty years ago I would not have considered Shakespearean tragedy, for example, or Hollywood epics, to be a promising subject-matter.

Similarly, the early experiences of listening to Percy French and Gilbert and Sullivan now seem to make sense, and the brilliant craftsmanship of writers from other traditions, such as Cole Porter, can be admired and envied, despite huge differences of style and background. The importance of craftsmanship, of technical competence, is something that strikes me more forcefully as the years go by. It seems a terrible waste to have a good idea for a song and to see it spoiled by sloppy construction, lazy or clichéd rhymes, or bad editing which allows the song to drift aimlessly towards the point where it loses its impact and its audience. In Ireland at present we are fortunate to have many outstanding songwriters in various idioms: among my own favourites, apart from those mentioned already, are John Spillane (along with his Gaelic Hit Factory colleague, Louis de Paor) and Mick Hanly.

I owe a huge debt to many people who have encouraged me and laughed at my songs over the past thirty years, not to mention all those songwriters, past and present, known and anonymous, whose works unwittingly inspired (or provoked) me into action. I thank all those singers, some of whom I don't even know, who sing my songs: their decision to do so is the ultimate accolade.

I am very grateful to Craft Recordings, who generously agreed to fund this project. Thanks to Terry Moylan, who first proposed the idea of a songbook to me and who has given much of his time to editing this volume. I am indebted to Pat "Herring" Ahern, who produced and engineered the accompanying CD, as well as playing on two of the tracks, and to Johnny McCarthy, who plays on Track 12. The marvellous drawings by Édaín O'Donnell add greatly to the quality of the book, and I thank her for her wonderful work.

For encouragement, and for giving me a platform from which to inflict my songs on the public on various occasions, I must thank Cork Singers' Club and Cork Folk Festival, especially Jim Walsh: the Góilín Singers' Club in Dublin; Gary Pepper and his committee in Feakle, Co. Clare: and Áine Meirbhic and Skibbereen Singers' Club.

Tom Munnelly, Máire Ní Chéileachair, Eoiní Ó Súilleabháin and Rachel Ní Riada are among those who gave me information on the airs of some of these songs. I thank Con Collins for his valuable advice. Táim buíoch de mhórán daoine i Múscraí a thug eolas, amhráin, lóistín agus misneach dom le blianta fada anuas, go h-áirithe Hammy agus Nóirín Hamilton agus muintir Shúilleabháin go léir.

Thanks to John Creedon, Donna O'Sullivan, Áine Hensey, Paula Carroll, Peter Browne, Tim Coughlan and Kieran Hanrahan, all of whom helped to bring the songs to a wider audience: to Jerry and Anne O'Reilly, Herring and Gloria Ahern, Johnny and Ger McCarthy, and Mick Willis for years of friendship, hospitality and encouragement.

Finally, a sincere thanks to my own family, especially my wife Gabriella for her patience and constant support.

A Dog's Life

With songs such as "The Armoured Car" and "The Killeens Hunt", Cork, like many places, has its share of doggy songs, though most of them seem to be songs of praise penned in honour of greyhounds, beagles or other sporting canines. Many of them, especially the first-mentioned, have a strong element of humour. The best comic dog song I know is George Curtin's "My Pup Came Home from Claodach", a masterpiece of mock-heroic verse in two languages. "Bob's Song" is my humble contribution to the canine canon.

Bob is a mongrel whose appearance stimulates much speculation; everyone who sees him has a theory on his ancestry; the majority mention the presence of some Jack Russell genes, although the nearest thoroughbred in appearance is probably the Patterdale terrier. Our first dog had been killed by a car. Our second, a beautiful Springer, threatened to savage our two sons and also ate holes in the back door, so she had to go. Then came Bob, a sorry-looking creature we got in the Dogs' Home (correctly titled Cork Society for the Prevention of Cruelty to Animals), with the information that he had been picked up on the street and was due for execution in two days' time if someone didn't offer him a home. We snatched him from Death Row and he prospered. Being responsible pet-owners, we got him neutered shortly after his arrival.

A few nights after Bob's operation, we happened to invite some friends to the house, and after dinner we were sitting around, chatting and sipping. Bob was on the sitting-room floor, sadly trying to lick what should have been there but no longer was, and his sorry plight was one of the subjects under discussion. Johnny McCarthy was idly picking out a few notes on the guitar, and then, to the amusement of the company, he started to sing a version of "Me and Bobby McGee" with words suitably adapted to our dog's plight. The thought struck me that a mock lament telling of Bob's trauma could be a good comic song.

The air is a very familiar one which has been used, with variations, in dozens of songs in Irish and in English. When I chose it, I was thinking mainly of "The Hide-and-go-Seek", a charming little song that I first heard sung by the late Maidhcí Ó Súilleabháin from Cúil Aodha, who died in 1976. Maidhcí was a regular performer, and a huge influence, in Seán Ó Riada's Claisceadal Chúil Aodha, and had a large store of songs. His sons and daughters have inherited and passed on those songs in fine manner. Seán Máistir Ó hIarlaithe, father of the famous Bess Cronin, composed "The Hide-and-go-Seek", about a hundred years ago. It is no coincidence that half of the songs in this book use airs usually associated with the West Muskerry district (with its natural hinterland which includes places such as Glenflesk and Glanlea). Since I first heard singers from Cúil Aodha and Baile Mhúirne in the late sixties, I have been fascinated by their style of singing, the number of fine comic songs the area has produced in both languages, and the best singers' special skill in highlighting the comic element in the songs. "Bob's Song" owes much, in its own humble way, to the Muskerry tradition, especially to that wonderful custom of fashioning a fine song out of an apparently insignificant event.

BOB

Bob's Song

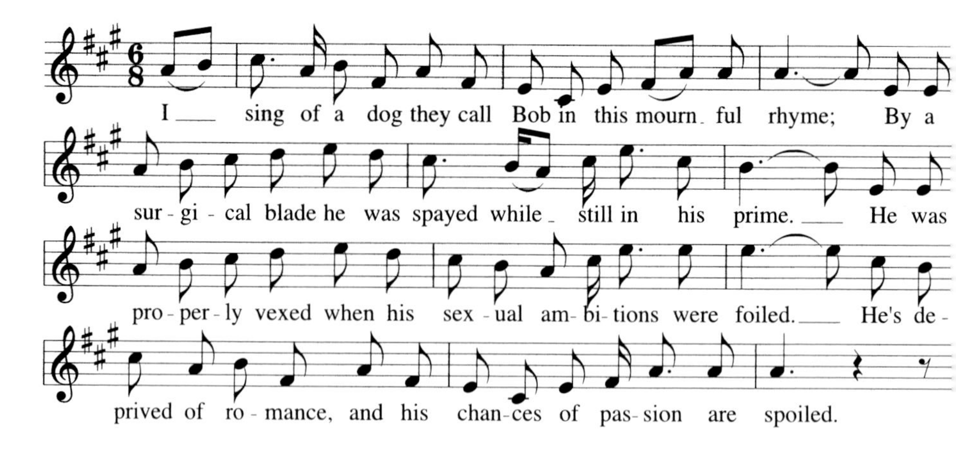

I sing of a dog they call Bob in this mournful rhyme;
By a surgical blade he was spayed while still in his prime.
He was properly vexed when his sexual ambitions were foiled,
He's deprived of romance, and his chances of passion are spoiled.

In his youth he had sport, and he courted with vigour and joy;
His fine apparatus had status that reached to the sky.
The grandest young bitches were itching to have him for life.
But they've all disappeared since his spheres were removed by the knife.

He put up with no slurs from those curs who came looking for fight:
One growl at those whelps, and they'd yelp and directly take flight;
But since losing his cluster, he's flustered and shaking with fear;
With his courage gone limp, he's a wimp, without conjugal gear.

His technique was so suave, with palaver and personal charm;
His foreplay ensured they were lured to fall into his arms.
But since losing his tackle, he's rattled, upset and dismayed;
With no tunes in his flute, the poor brute can no longer get laid.

A man came the way yesterday with his bitch to get poked;
He'd heard that our hound was renowned for the strength of his yoke.
I said "Sorry, you're late, and your fate with misfortune is crowned,
Since our Bobbie got neutered his shooter can't fire any rounds".

Of the day he was gelded I'll tell, though your nerves will be shot.
He was lying on a slab when a jab of the needle he got.
There were vets and attendants resplendent in surgical robes,
Then with one rapid snip, out they whipped his connubial globes.

So how can a mutt without nuts have a future that's great?
Without utensils nuptial, no pup shall he e'er procreate.
Since losing his fittings, he's quitting romantic affairs,
For the skill to seduce is no use when there's nothing downstairs.

So the days when this codger could roger all round him have ceased;
He won't couple again with the shin of our old parish priest.
He's trying medical potions and lotions that seep through his pores,
His appliance to refuel, for his jewels he expects to restore.

Entomological Exploits

The July trip to Scoil Shamhraidh Willie Clancy has been a feature of my life for a quarter of a century. In the early eighties it took the form of a camping trip, and the routine was to arrive in Miltown Malbay on Sunday or Monday afternoon, pitch the tent in some field close to town, and spend the week playing music, having long and frequently ridiculous conversations with like-minded characters from all over Ireland and elsewhere, and trying to ensure our favourite publicans, such as Tom Queally and Paddy Hennessy, made enough money to guarantee their survival through the lean winter months. In recent years the onset of middle age has seen many of us shortening the week considerably, sleeping in beds, eating, and generally taking the soft option. I sometimes feel a crazy pang of guilt at not doing the full week of hardship and outright debauchery, much as a cheating Lough Derg pilgrim must feel as he surreptitiously wires into the ham sandwiches he smuggled onto the island.

One part of my "Willie Week" routine that was sacred for many years was to spend the first session of each day (usually from midday to four in the afternoon) in Hennessy's bar with Johnny O'Leary and the Sliabh Luachra brigade. We played tunes for hours, interspersed with Johnny's earthy yarns and the odd song, and invariably sets were danced to Johnny's invigorating music. I learned dozens of tunes from Johnny, and got to know great and memorable characters such as the late Pa Keane and Dan O'Keeffe. They, along with our host Paddy Hennessy and Johnny himself, have all left us since then, and Hennessy's bar is but a memory.

One July in the early eighties I arrived in town on Monday afternoon, and met the Sliabh Luachra team as they headed for their quarters in a house on the Flag Road. Eily Buckley (who has also composed a few songs over the years) insisted that I pitch my tent in the back garden, and I didn't decline the invitation: the prospect of a dose of Johnny Leary yarns over breakfast, in addition to my usual ration in Hennessy's, was too tempting. I found that the back garden was something of a wilderness, but I trampled the long grass and put up the tent. Unfortunately the combination of heavy vegetation and damp weather meant that the garden was thickly populated with God's creatures. I woke in the small hours of one morning to feel something nipping my elbow, and on inspection I found a black beetle sharing my sleeping bag. I ejected the little chap, gently made it clear he shouldn't come back, and slept on.

The song took shape slowly over several days, but its birth was hastened by the pub conversations that quickly gave arms and legs to the original story, and by the time I left for home the new, spectacular versions of the event had supplanted the humble original in my imagination. I used the air (with a slight variation) of "The Trip to Guagán", a fine comic song written by John Brown, who also wrote "The Kilnamartyra Exile". I have fond memories of the late Diarmuidín Ó Súilleabháin singing "The Trip" in Abbeyfeale on the night of my wedding.

I recorded "The Miltown Cockroach" on the Four Star Trio's 1997 album, *The Square Triangle.* Since then it has been recorded by Diarmuid Grainger on a Natural Gas album, and I am very happy to note that many other fine singers have included it in their repertoire, including Séamus

Creagh and Rosie Stewart. Hearing one's song taking on a life of its own and spreading around the country is the most satisfying thing that can happen a songwriter. Muiris Ó Rócháin, director of Scoil Shamhraidh Willie Clancy, once told me that he met an academic from Newfoundland who had never heard of Willie Clancy or of the Summer School, but had heard of Miltown Malbay as the habitat of the cockroach. The clue which made sense of this story was the fact that Séamus Creagh had lived in Newfoundland for a year.

The Miltown Cockroach

Oh, the west County Clare is a beautiful place,
Its people a charming and musical race.
'Tis pleasant to view it by car or by coach,
But a blot on the landscape is the Miltown Cockroach.
Rally-ra fol the doh, rally-rah fol the dee.

The Miltown Cockroach is a martyr for beer,
His eye it is evil, his aspect severe;
He barks like a bulldog and kicks like a mule,
And he drinks and he fights and he plays games of pool . . .

In sweet Miltown Malbay, one night in July,
I retired to my tent as the sunrise was nigh;
Established in comfort with grunts and with yawns,
I shortly was dreaming of tunes and *rabhcáns* . . .

But I woke with a start after two hours or so
To a loud crunching noise coming from my big toe:

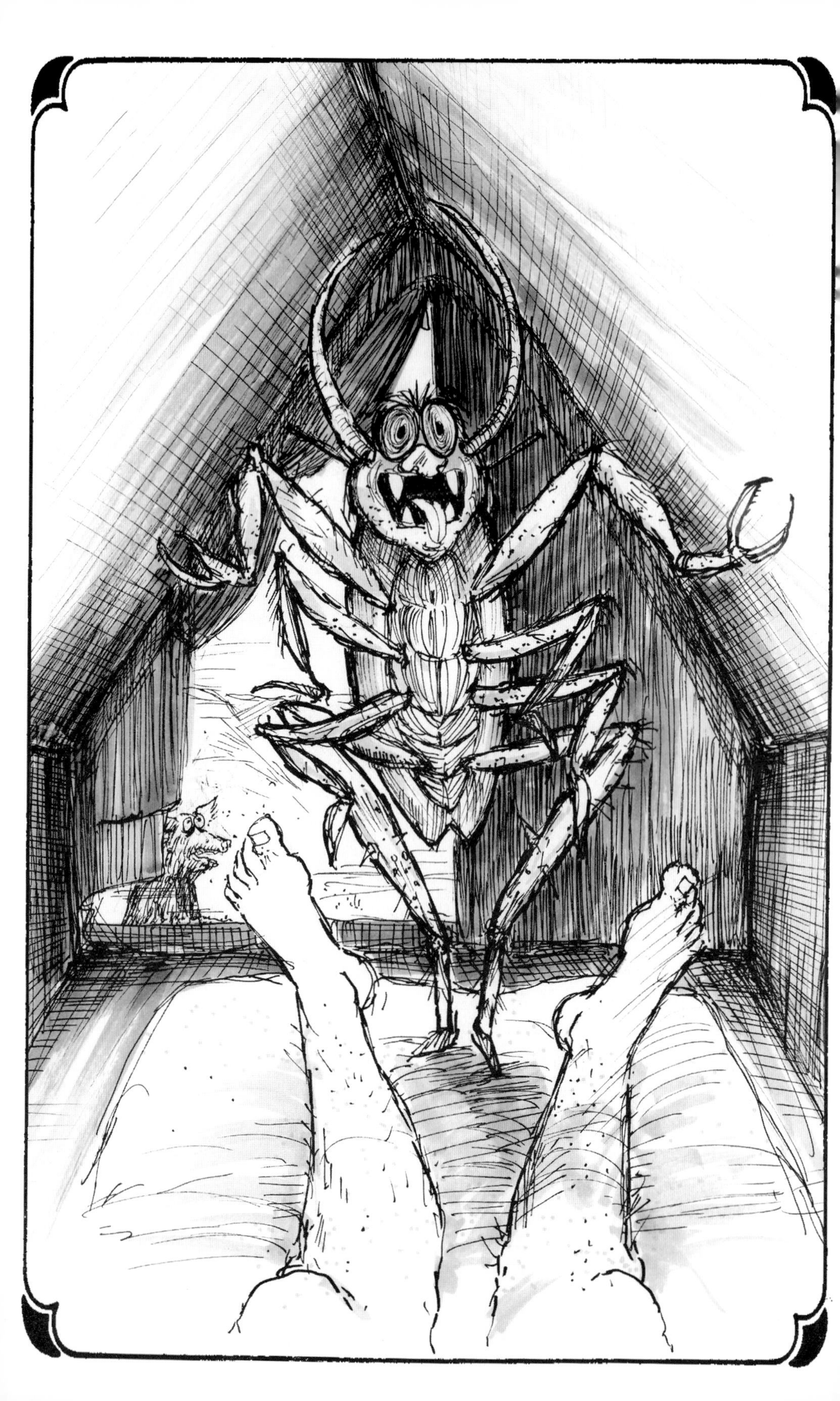

This insect most foul then came into my view,
On the sole of my foot he proceeded to chew . . .

So I jumped from the bed with a terrible screech,
Saying "Mister Cockroach, of the law you're in breach;
On a citizen's blood you may not slake your thirst
Without gaining the donor's approval at first" . . .

"Of the legal position", says he, "I have doubt,
For this blood is at least fifty-eight percent stout:
So stop quoting law, and lie down again quick
Till myself and my buddies conclude our picnic" . . .

So I tried to sweet-talk him with eloquent chat,
Saying "a gourmet like you can do better than that:
Look at my carcass, 'tis scrawny and tough,
While of plump tender youths there are surely enough" . . .

Says the Cockroach, "you speak like a poet and a sage,
But truly you don't taste too bad for your age.
My friends have decided that here we will dine;
While the meat isn't great, sure the pickle is fine" . . .

So I tackled those insects with brain and with brawn;
We struggled and tore at each other till dawn.
I fought them with blows and with bites and with kicks,
I tried burning and drowning and all sorts of tricks . . .

But that offspring of Satan came at me in gangs,
Snarling and showing me their venomous fangs.
They crawled from the ditches and out of the sewers,
Ten thousand or more of them six-legged hoors . . .

They covered the ground like a black shiny sheet,
Till I knew it was time for to sound the retreat;
I turned and ran, full of loathing and dread,
And from sweet Miltown Malbay that morning I fled . . .

Oh, the black widow spider is not a nice toy,
And the African cobra is one ugly boy;
But both of them surely are cuddly and fair
Compared to the man-eating Cockroach from Clare . .

The Percussionist from Hell

The murder ballad is a scary sort of convention in traditional song. Usually English, Scottish or American, it tells of crimes of passion, of jealousy, of revenge. Very often the victim is a fair young maid. It is a doom-laden genre, which seems to accept that the characters, both victim and killer, are in the grip of some destiny that leaves them with little choice.

Tim Lyons is the only other songwriter I know who wrote a comic murder ballad. His masterpiece, "The Murder of Joe Frawley", is full of perceptive detail about small-town Irish life, and it also departs from tradition by having a female murderer and a male victim. When I first heard Tim's song, one Sunday morning many years ago in Kilgarvan, the notion lodged somewhere in my mind that comic murder ballads are rare and that it would be nice to write one some time. As with many projects in many people's minds, it lay there, dormant, for years. Then I heard the story from my Four Star Trio colleagues of an encounter they had one night with a spoons-player who disrupted their tunes and who was incapable of taking a hint, however broad or unsubtle.

The phenomenon of the unwanted session member is familiar to all who play music in informal settings. Musicians are sometimes accused of being elitist, of not giving the novice a chance to experience a session and to learn the ropes. Most experienced musicians I know are very welcoming to the newcomer, and will make every effort to accommodate him or her. There are certain obvious rules, however, that musicians with a bit of common sense don't need to be taught. For example, when joining a session you should ask the existing members if they mind having you; when in, you don't try to dominate, to dictate the pace and the tune selection; and most obviously, you don't try to play tunes you don't know, spoiling the enjoyment for everyone else. Clearly, if playing an accompanying instrument of any kind, you ensure that you aren't louder than the melody.

Any player of any instrument who follows these simple rules of good sense and politeness will fit easily enough into any music session. Having said that, I must state that I have never heard a spoons-player who has added in any way to the music. Even if he/she has perfect rhythm, the sad fact is that the very sound of these implements has nothing to do with making music, and everything to do with spoiling it and distracting from it. So while I wasn't actually present on the Night of the Spoons-Player from Hell, I had more than enough bad memories to enable me to visualise the scene; one that comes to mind immediately is an afternoon pub gig we played during a festival in Cornwall, when we were surrounded by seven bodhrán players who were so loud and insensitive that when we stopped in mid-tune they all kept pounding away happily.

So I had found the perfect, deserving victim for my murder ballad, and all that had to be decided was the weapon. I cannot give any rational explanation for the choice of weapon in this case. Maybe I subconsciously wanted something more outrageous than Tim Lyons's "Black Diamond banjo wire". Maybe my youthful obsession with Flann O'Brien's writings put the idea of the bicycle in my mind. At any rate, one of the pleasures of writing fiction, whether story or song, is that you can do what you like; if the audience enjoys the result, that's all the justification a writer needs. This attitude also led me to decide that I wasn't going to swing, fry or even do time for this spoons-player: thus the deliberately contrived happy ending, which is most untypical of murder ballads.

The air is that of "The Lass with the Bonny Brown Hair", a fine love song that has been recorded by Dublin singer Phil Callery, among others.

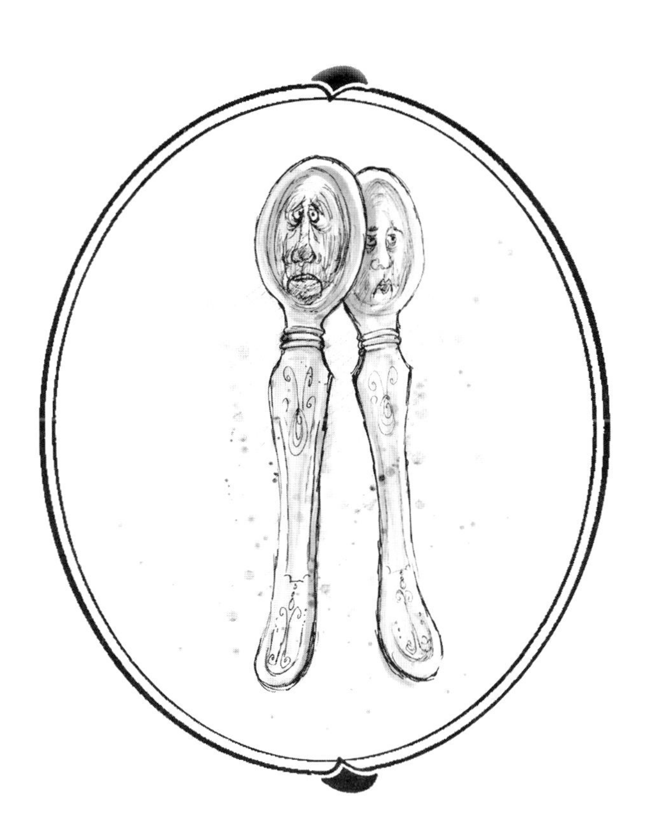

The Spoons Murder

In the tavern one night we were sitting –
    I'm sure 'twas the last week of March –
From our drinks we were cautiously sipping
    To ensure that our throats didn't parch.
We played music both lively and dacent
    To bolster our spirits and hopes,
As we gazed on the females adjacent
    And remarked on their curves and their slopes.

Till this gent wandered into the session
And decided to join in the tunes;
Without waiting to ask our permission
He took out a big pair of soup spoons.
Our teeth in short time we were gritting
As he shook and he rattled his toys,
And the company's eardrums were splitting
With his ugly mechanical noise.

Hopping spoons off our heads to provoke us,
He continued the music to kill;
Whether hornpipes, slow airs or polkas,
They all sounded like pneumatic drills.
Then he asked could we play any faster,
As his talent he wished to display,
With a grin on the face of the bastard
Like the cat when she teases her prey.

Our thoughts at this stage were quite bloody
And politely we asked him to quit;
We suggested a part of his body
Where those spoons could conveniently fit.
This monster we pestered and hounded,
We implored him with curses and tears,
But in vain our appeals they resounded
In the desert between his two ears.

When I went out the back on a mission,
He arrived as I finished my leak;
He says "This is a mighty fine session,
I think I'll come here every week".
When I heard this, with rage I was leppin',
And this torture no longer I'd take:
I looked round for a suitable weapon
To silence this damned rattlesnake.

Outside towards the yard I did sally
To find something to vanquish my foe:
I grabbed hold of a gentleman's Raleigh
With fifteen-speed gear and dynamo.
Then I battered that musical vandal
As I shouted with furious cries
"My dear man, your last spoon you have handled,
Say your prayers and await your demise!"

With the bike I assailed my tormentor
As I swung in a frenzy of hate,
Till his bones and his skull were in splinters
And his health in a very poor state.
And when I was no longer able,
I forestalled any last-minute hitch
By removing the gear-changing cable
And strangling that son-of-a-bitch.

At the end of my onslaught ferocious
I stood back and surveyed the scene;
The state of the place was atrocious,
Full of fragments of man and machine.
At the spoons-player's remains I was staring,
His condition was surely no joke,
For his nose was clogged up with ball-bearings
And his left eye was pierced by a spoke.

At the sight I was feeling quite squeamish,
So I washed up and went back inside;
Then I drank a half-gallon of Beamish,
As my throat in the struggle had dried.
Unpolluted by cutlery's clatter
The music was pleasant and sweet;
For the rest of the night nothing mattered
But the tunes and the tapping of feet.

At an inquest, the following September,
        The coroner said "I conclude
The deceased by himself was dismembered,
        As no sign could be found of a feud.
For the evidence shows that the fact is,
        As reported to me by the guards,
He indulged in the foolhardy practice
        Of trick-cycling in public house yards".

So if you're desperately keen on percussion,
        And to join in the tunes you can't wait;
Be you Irishman, German or Russian,
        Take a lesson from his awful fate.
If your spoons are the best silver-plated,
        Or the humblest of cheap stainless steel,
When you play them abroad you'll be hated,
        So just keep them for eating your meals.

Bould Thady on Wheels

General Lew Wallace started it all in 1880 when he published his novel *Ben-Hur: a Tale of the Christ.* The novel was such a success that it was adapted for the stage in 1899, and opened on Broadway, complete with chariot race live on stage. The silent movie came in 1925, directed by Fred Niblo and starring Ramon Navarro in the title role, and the big one, William Wyler's four-hour epic, was released in 1959. It still turns up on TV schedules every Christmas, and I like to tune in three hours after the start, in time to catch the chariot race while gladly missing the earnest, ponderous build-up. It has lost some of its magic in recent years, mainly due to my aversion to Charlton Heston and his prominence in America's gun lobby. In fact, I really wouldn't mind if Messala were to beat him next Christmas.

As is the case with many enterprises, inspiration often comes via the juxtaposition of two or more thoughts which had not previously met in the mind. Thus my long-held ambition to write a parody of the classic murder ballads came suddenly to mind when taking part in a conversation about unwelcome guests (especially of the percussive persuasion) in a music session, and the cross-breeding of the two ideas led to "The Spoons Murder". "Ben Hur" had a similar genesis. The sporting ballad, especially the comic variety of which "Bould Thady Quill" must be the greatest example, was somewhere in my subconscious as a type waiting to be exploited, but whenever the idea came to the surface I shied away from it. Being by nature a cautious character, I pick my victims carefully: I like them to be safely dead, like St. Finbarr, or anonymous, like the spoons player, or totally fictitious, like Ben Hur, or dumb animals, as in the cockroach and Bob the dog.

The idea of marrying the traditional sporting ballad with the Hollywood Biblical epic was given to me unintentionally by Paudie O'Connor, that fine box-player from Ballyhar, Co. Kerry. I got to know Paudie a few years ago through our shared passion for Sliabh Luachra music, and especially our admiration and affection for the late Johnny O'Leary. Paudie is an expert in the science of betting, and I value very highly his knowledge of sport and his instinct for picking winners. As I left Croke Park after the 2004 All-Ireland Hurling semi-final, I was worried that Cork had had it too easy against Wexford, and that it wasn't the greatest preparation for a Final battle with our great rivals from Kilkenny. So in the middle of Jones's Road I stopped and texted Paudie, looking for reassurance. The reply came promptly: "Cork are the surest thing since Ben Hur". As usual, he was right.

The seed of the song was sown there, in August, but it didn't germinate until the following Christmas week, when I saw the movie listed for 2:00pm in RTÉ's schedule, and duly sat down at 5:10 to catch the race. Then it clicked. Why not write the story of the chariot race in the style of the heroic sporting ballads? Ridiculous? The more ridiculous the better, I thought, and the job began. Being a sporting ballad, it had to have hyperbole and heroics: the good guy had to beat the baddie, who (of course) had been the odds-on favourite: and there had to be some political overtones to add spice and spite to the proceedings. Lew Wallace had already provided all of this, and the way was open for me to play with language and to mess around to my heart's content with outrageous rhymes and anachronisms, as well as drawing on my knowledge of the Gospels (one of the advantages of having been educated in Catholic Ireland in the fifties and sixties) to augment the cast of characters.

The air is that of "Sarah Jane", a lovely song recorded by The Voice Squad, who got it via Frank Harte from the repertoire of Eddie Butcher from Magilligan, Co. Derry.

Ben Hur

You may chatter and sing of Mackey and Ring and the greats of the hurling game,
Of athletes bold who compete for gold and footballers of great fame:
Of horses like Arkle who galloped and sparkled, and followers' hearts did stir:
But the charioteer who knew no fear was the driver they called Ben Hur.

In his youth he was a force at water sports, at Olympus he swam for Rome;

He excelled at rowing with a style so flowing as his boat skimmed
across the foam.
His career aquatic by a leg rheumatic was ended, despite his fame,
So he bought an ould chariot from Judas Iscariot and tried out the racing game.

In 32 A.D. it happened to be that Messala was Empire champ;
A scheming fiend full of bile and spleen, an unprincipled lowdown
tramp.
At equine auctions this type obnoxious could buy any horse he
pleased,
For he knew that all the while it was Pontius Pilate, his sponsor, who
paid the fees.

One night it did occur that he met Ben Hur in a bar in downtown
Beirut:
Messala was rowdy and talking loudly, he bragged of his high repute;
So Ben walked up and he says "You're a pup, a despicable cheating
thug,
You always come first for your nags are nursed with performance-enhancing drugs".

Messala he quaffed from his pint and laughed as he said to his nasty
mates,
"I swear by Pythagoras, this dirty little shagger is foolishly tempting
fate;
We Roman players are strong and fair, and at racing we are the best;
But in the four-o'-clock at Antioch your words you can truly test".

So the challenge was met and they laid their bets and the fixture was
advertised;
Centurions and majors were laying big wagers Messala would claim
first prize.
Not even his brother would chance a little flutter on Ben Hur as an
each-way pick,
And the racing cognoscenti declared in print he surely wouldn't do the
trick.

All the pubs were chock-a-block in Antioch on the morning of this great race:
It was all sold out, and the shady touts of a ticket could find no trace.
There were fast-food stalls all around the walls, where the customers stood in queues,
And a girl called Vera from Al-Jazeera conducted the interviews.

So the drivers' first task was to follow the Damascus Loyal Volunteer Pipe Band;
Those Syrians and Zionists dressed in their finest were cheering from terrace and stand.
In the dearest seating the Romans were eating sandwiches filled with prawns,
For they all came to the gala supporting Messala, their very own *buachaill bán.*

With Messala and Ben there were three more men who went to the starting line:
Some die-hard punters had money on Gunther, a Hun from beyond the Rhine;
A brave Mesopotamian whose name was Damien was seen as an also-ran,
And a chap called Lazarus whose driving was hazardous excited the local fans.

The moment they got started, bould Lazarus darted like mad for the opening bend:
With a desperate swerve he tackled the curve, but his chariot did upend;
As he lay in his gore there remained just four until Damien lost the head:
When all his plans unravelled, through the air he travelled till he landed up in Row Z.

Then moving to the front was the valiant Gunther exhorting his eager steeds;
Messala was chasing, his eyes were blazing, determined on evil deeds.

With his big long whip, one horse he tripped and the Hun from his chariot threw;
Then with his horrid smile Ben Hur he riled, saying "the next one to die is you".

So they galloped side by side and Messala tried his rival to intimidate;
He pushed right in and he crowded Ben who shouted at him "watch it, mate!
You're putting us in danger, you half-witted langer, your horses on dope are high!"
He knew disaster beckoned for whoever came second, so his choice was to win or die.

Through all the dust and smoke Ben Hur then spoke to his thoroughbred broncos four:
He talked about pagan invaders plaguing his people, who suffered right sore.
"There's no freedom to be had without another jihad, we'll strike for our libertee,
And we'll clear the Middle East of these greedy beasts, or we'll die in the fray", says he.

Then his noble horses charged and on they barged as the enemy they shoved aside;
Messala was humbled, his thoroughbreds stumbled, their energies all had dried.
From his chariot falling, his fate was appalling, being battered by hooves and wheels;
In the course of all this skirmish, his torn epidermis came off like potato peels.

So the race was in the bag, and past the chequered flag Ben Hur and his team came in:
Those joyful Israelis were drinking rum and Baileys, to celebrate a noble win.
The ambulance brigade were giving first aid with Messala's own backroom team,

And a specialist from Babylon was rubbing on Savlon soothing anti-
septic cream.

But of those gallant drivers, the only survivor was Ben, with the laurel
crowned:
For all of his rivals with ceremonies tribal were laid in the burial
ground.
Only Lazarus's folks complained they were broke, saying "the undertaker we can't pay,
For we buried him already but instead of staying dead he turned up for
his dinner next day".

In Praise of Pipers

People seem to create or accept stereotyped images of each other very easily, whatever their field of interest. Hurling men have a traditional image in their heads of the brawny full-back or the nippy corner-forward. In the school staffroom, we don't expect to confuse the middle-aged History or English teacher (corduroys and pullovers and strong views on whatever is in today's newspaper) with the Woodwork man (shop coat and a few building projects on the side). In music, the piper is classically seen as a bit odd; an eccentric, cranky, temperamental type who has been set apart from the rest of humanity by the long years he has spent perfecting the art of playing a ridiculously complex instrument. Most people are familiar with the jibe that defines a gentleman as "someone who can play the pipes but doesn't". Above all other traditional Irish instruments, the uilleann pipes are identified as a solo instrument: pipers have rarely been considered part of a céilí band line-up, for example.

As with all stereotypes, this image of the piper bears little, if any, relation to the truth. I know some pipers who are a little odd, but then I also know a few fiddle-players, accordionists, flute-players, singers and bodhrán-beaters whom I'd hardly recommend as models of emotional equilibrium.

"The Irish Piper" was commissioned by one of the aforesaid gentlemen (and editor of this book), Terry Moylan of Na Píobairí Uilleann, in June 2004. His request was for a humorous song about pipers, and I worked on it during that summer and autumn, giving the first public performance during a song weekend in Miltown Malbay the following November. The tone is mock-heroic: I tried to strike a balance between praising the piper and mocking him, while being aware that such a balance is impossible to achieve; if you put a full-page advertisement in the papers declaring that your local T.D. is not a corrupt rogue, the resulting impression will not necessarily be a positive one. This spurious attempt at balance, however, can be turned to comic effect, and this is what I hope I have done in the song.

The air will be recognised as a variation on "The Bould Thady Quill", pushing it away from the waltz time in which that song is usually sung, and reshaping it as a jig. Mícheál Marrinan's fine comic song "The Binder Twine" uses a similar air. It seems quite likely to me that many song airs of the same vintage as "Bould Thady" may have originated as jigs.

The Irish Piper

You grand connoisseurs of fine reels and slow airs,
A few moments you'll spare to give ear to my croon;
Till without inhibition I praise a musician
Adept and proficient at all kinds of tunes.
For a sound that's heart-stopping, a rhythm that's topping,
For cranning and popping with flair and with style,
From east of the Khyber to the banks of the Tiber
You won't beat the piper from Erin's green isle.

This piper contrives with his elbow to drive
Some fresh air which arrives in a bag 'neath his arm;

PIPERUS
MAXIMUS
PMXXXOO7

He fingers the chanter as lithe as a panther,
No sound could be grander for beauty and charm.
When the air it is blown through the finely-tuned drones
It produces a tone that amazes the ear:
Regulators get going as a musical bonus,
With notes so harmonious, perfection is near.

I sing no encomium for pipes Caledonian
Which cannot be blown on inside in the house,
For your bagpiper Scottish must leave his own cottage,
His unhappy lot is to play for the cows.
As he stands in the rain with his lungs under strain,
All his work is in vain, as the gale hoists his kilt.
He can blow till he's crocked, but his way will be blocked,
For to play a high octave his pipes are not built.

Some people declare that all pipers are quare
With a manner that scares timid people and weans.
Their behaviour so strange and their wits half-deranged,
As if some sort of mange infiltrated their brains.
Playing those pipes problematic takes skills acrobatic
Which turn them fanatic, obsessive and grim:
So these cynics deride all his properties vital,
To slander our idol's their purpose and whim.

For howe'er they may slight him, our hero's a Titan,
A brave gallant knight and a champion supreme;
Though he's often attacked as being thorny as cactus
He's not half as cracked as he sometimes may seem.
He's bright and flamboyant, his heart's full of joy and
He's almost clairvoyant, with wisdom endowed;
He's keen as a razor when he starts Colonel Fraser
And he drives women crazier by playing Miss McLeod.

I could write an epistle on screechy tin whistles
Or the germ-filled drizzle that drips from the flute;
The tone-deaf accompanist happily thumping his
Strings, causing grumpiness, rows and disputes.

Those musical rookies who torture bouzoukis
Make noises so spooky, for mercy you'll plead;
Forget all those villains, your *píobaire uilleann*
Is famed for his brilliance at handling a reed.

So if your life is like slime and your verses won't rhyme
And the days of your prime are a memory frail,
Avoid treatments quixotic like drink or narcotics,
Just hear the hypnotic bagpipes of the Gael.
'Twould take Archimedes a hundred and three days
To grasp how that reed is created from cane.
But my powers they grow scanty, I'd need the poet Dante
Or the Spaniard Cervantes to sing this refrain.

Jig-Time Shakespeare

Ever since my teens, when Fr. Jerome Kiely, an inspiring English teacher, introduced us to *Julius Caesar* and *Hamlet*, I have had a great fondness for Shakespeare, especially his tragedies. Since then I have had the opportunity to teach some of his works to my own classes, and so it happened that around 1999 I had been working on *King Lear* with some students who, understandably, found it hard to accept that any intelligent human being could act as stupidly as Lear does in Act I.

That very summer we (The Four Star Trio) were playing at the Sidmouth Folk Festival, a huge international gathering in a pleasant seaside town in Devon, and one afternoon I heard the great Martin Carthy singing a version of *Hamlet* to the air of "The Mason's Apron". This brilliant comic song was written by Adam McNaughtan from Glasgow, of whom I hadn't heard previously, and it used outrageous rhymes and colloquial language to marvellous effect in tracing the play's convoluted story. A month later, back at the day job, and still facing the doubts of my English class regarding *King Lear's* far-fetched plot, it dawned on me that I really wanted to have a go at making a comic song of *Lear*.

Using the well-known jig "Tatter Jack Walsh" as an air, I got to work.

Writing comic songs isn't always fun, and can be a nerve-wracking experience. What seems funny to me sitting in front of the computer may not necessarily work for an audience, and is even less likely to amuse the solitary listener to the CD or tape. Doubts arise constantly, blind alleys are entered and quickly reversed out of, the eloquent phrase (that I simply must use!) won't fit the metre, or won't rhyme with anything and has to be discarded. The hackneyed saying about "ten per cent inspiration and ninety per cent perspiration" comes constantly to mind. To compensate, there comes the thought that, in the past, lines that seemed pretty ordinary to me often drew louder laughs from the audience than some of what I thought were my best ones.

Writing "King Lear" proved easier than I had anticipated, however. I could deal with some characters in a line, and many of Shakespeare's characters disappeared completely. The plot is so outrageous that I didn't need to do much to make it funny. Stripped of Shakespeare's brilliant language, his plots are usually far-fetched, just as grand opera's plots are often quite ridiculous when read without great music to make them palatable. Messing around with rhymes is great fun, and the freedom to use a mixture of formal and colloquial language can in itself be a comic tool.

Some time after I had written and sung the song, Paul Dromey, music critic, lent me a CD of Adam McNaughtan which included his version of *Macbeth* in a hornpipe tempo, entitled (of course) "The Scottish Song". Since then I've heard other gems from the same pen, including his marvellous anti-health-food song, called "Cholesterol". One of the pleasant perks of writing comic songs is getting the chance to hear great songwriters and even meeting them.

Finally, the obligatory health warning: more than one parent has asked me to send the words of "King Lear" to their sons or daughters who were studying the play for their exams. Though sorely tempted to grab the chance of selling a CD, I reply that whether they like it or not, Shakespeare's version, not mine, is the one on their course; and furthermore, Shakespeare made a classic work of literature out of this story, one that will last long after my cheap laughs will be forgotten.

King Lear

You scholars of English, one question I'll ask;
To answer you won't find a difficult task;
Of Shakespeare's great heroes, which one would you pick
To award him first prize for being totally thick?
Othello you know was a gullible dupe,
And Hamlet's delaying landed him in the soup;
But the stupidest asshole in all of Shakespeare
Is that old king of England, the man they call Lear.

Three daughters he had in the course of his life,
Although we're not told what befell his poor wife;

KL
DAD

I'll bet she ran off to avoid going insane
After years of enduring that pompous ould pain.
At the Donkey and Crown where he drank every night,
The locals all knew poor old Lear wasn't bright;
When they said "Your Royal Highness we love and revere",
The old fool lapped it up and bought everyone beer.

At the age of four score, and in fear of expiring,
King Lear told his girls he intended retiring;
Of loss of his faculties sadly he moaned,
As if he could forfeit what he never owned.
He told them his kingdom he planned to partition
Provided his daughters fulfilled one condition;
"I won't hand you over this rich legacy,
Till you tell me how much you admire me", says he.

Now the two eldest daughters, called Goneril and Regan,
Knew well what he wanted, so promptly they began
To swear how they always did love and respect him,
They thought the sun rose every day from his rectum.
Says Cordelia, the youngest, being honest and true,
"Can't you see, Dad, they're taking the piss out of you?"
King Lear lost the head and began to scream at her,
But still she refused her old father to flatter.

In a rage the bould Lear says "I swear on my honour I'll
Split my estate between Regan and Gonerile;
Nothing for Delia, no land nor finance,
She can pack her belongings and shag off to France".
If that's not bad enough, that pathetic old jerk
Left himself without house, without income or perk;
The two vixens took all, and their Dad, the old dunce,
Was to lodge in their houses in alternate months.

These daughters quite clearly were nasty old shrews,
But in fairness King Lear gave them every excuse;
His boiled eggs were too hard and his gravy too thin,

Or he got too much tonic and not enough gin.
So they both found their dad an unbearable bore;
Ere the first month was finished they showed him the door;
In those far-off days there was no county home,
So old Lear like a tramp 'round the country did roam.

Up to this he was lacking in guile and in craft,
But now the old geezer went totally daft;
He ran through the fields and he crawled through the bogs,
He was screaming and howling and barking at dogs.
But in spite of his faults and ridiculous foibles
He still had a band of devoted disciples;
Young Edgar was there, and the loyal Duke of Kent,
And a man called the Fool, quite a sensible gent!

One other wayfarer I'll add to this roster;
'Twas Edgar's blind father, the old Duke of Gloucester;
He disowned his son who he thought was untrue,
In fact Lear and himself were of equal I.Q.
Then they heard the news, as they wandered all over,
Cordelia arrived off the ferry in Dover;
Being now queen of France, she assembled an army
Avenging her da, when she heard he was barmy.

So thousands of men in the battle were slaughtered
And victory went to the two vicious daughters;
But they never got to be powerful and rich,
Overcome as they were by a lecherous itch.
For Edgar's half-brother they both wished to own;
The same man for the power of his pelvis was known;
So one of them poisoned the other one's lager,
Then did for herself with a seven-inch dagger.

Since tragedies must have their audience crying,
There followed a terrible outbreak of dying;
Edgar stabbed his half-brother, that devious crook,
And the shock killed his daddy, that's Gloucester's old Duke.

Cordelia was hanged by a treacherous jailer,
Lear died when it struck him that he was a failure;
If he only had snuffed it a few years before,
He'd have saved everybody this suffering and gore.

Sink or Swim

Tocane Saint Apre is a small town in the Dordogne district of France, the sort of town many of us would never have heard of but for an accident of history. It so happened that a group of people, some natives of the area and some who came from outside to live there, came together in the 1980s to play Irish traditional music. Shortly afterwards, they decided to organise a small summer school in which French musicians, singers and dancers could learn the tunes, the songs, the dances and the skills needed to perform them. The first "Rencontre Musicale Irlandaise" took place in 1991, and a team of Irish musicians was invited over to do the teaching. Each year since then, the event has taken place in late July, and generally the teaching musicians are changed from year to year, giving the French students the chance to learn different regional styles. I had the honour of being "prof' d'accordeon" in 1992.

One of the remarkable features of Tocane is that many Irish people who were employed there enjoyed it so much that they regularly return on holidays: during the music week any July there are nine or ten Irish people busy teaching, and there are dozens of others, including myself, who just go along for fun: we appreciate the friends we have made there, the beautiful rolling countryside, the fine food and wine, and the fact that along with all that you also have the prospect of a few good music sessions. Could anyone ask for more?

Like most inland towns in France, Tocane uses what advantages it has. It lies on the banks of the river Dronne, a tributary of the Dordogne, and the *municipalité* has developed a little beach on the river-bank, where young and old alike can cool down on hot afternoons. During the week of "la Musique Irlandaise", the beach is a meeting point for Irish people.

It was there that I experienced a slight scare one day, when the river level was unusually high and the current was strong, following a few weeks of heavy rain. As a staunch non-swimmer, I was wading in the centre of the river when I found the current too strong, with the result that I was being pushed towards a point where I would have been out of my depth. I called for help, and three men who were in the water pushed me towards the shallows. They were piper Ronan Browne and flautist Desi Wilkinson, (two members of Cran), and Pat Carroll from Dublin, another inveterate Tocane-attender.

Need I say what happened next? As in the case of "The Miltown Cockroach", the story spread all over town, and grew and developed as stories always do. The song was an inevitable outcome, and as everyone else was exaggerating the story, why not do it myself? Messrs Browne and Wilkinson contributed ideas, mainly by sitting on the river-bank loudly reproaching themselves for saving a mere accordionist. In the song this inspired the mock vanity and self-importance which appears in some of the verses (the nation mourns, etc.). Andrew MacNamara, the Tulla accordion player, contributed the idea for the final verse when I met him in Feakle a few weeks later and he feigned terror, shouting "You're a ghost!"

The air is "Táimse ar an mBaile Seo", a song I often heard, and indeed sang, in Corca Dhuibhne. I associate it mainly with Dan Pheats Ó Catháin, originally from Cloichear, who came home to West Kerry every summer to renew acquaintances with his old friends and fishing colleagues.

Coincidentally, France gets a mention in that song as a centre of medical excellence:

Táimse ar an mbaile seo le bliain agus trí lá,
'S dá mbeadh fios mo scéil i gceart agaibh ní chodlódh sibh go sámh;
Dochtúirí na Fraince, ní leigheasfaidís mo chneá,
Go dtiocfaidh péarla an chúil chraobhaigh, 's go gcroithfidh sí mo lámh.

An Fear Báite

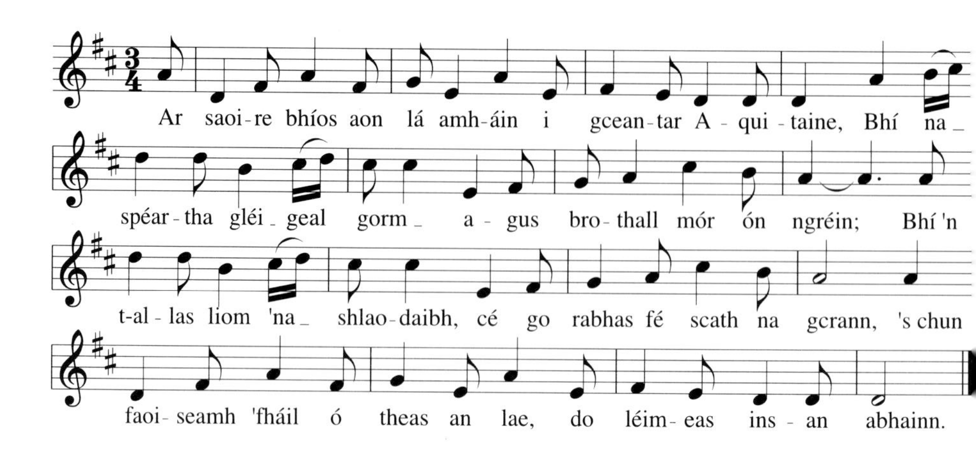

Ar saoire bhíos aon lá amháin i gceantar Aquitaine,
Bhí na spéartha gléigeal gorm agus brothall mór ón ngréin;
Bhí an t-allas liom 'na shlaodaibh, cé go rabhas fé scáth na gcrann,
Is chun faoiseamh 'fháil ó theas an lae, do léimeas insan abhainn.

The river Dronne so cool and clear revived my failing strength;
But its depth exceeded greatly my considerable length.
Away from friends and kindred by the torrent I was swept,
I could see them standing on the shore as helplessly they wept.

Bhí mo mhuintir bhocht ag béicigh, is ar chúnamh bhí ag glaoch,
'Sé dúirt siad, "An bhfuil éinne anso a thabharfaidh slán ár laoch?"
Bhí an ait 'na raic le h-olagón, le caoineadh is le gleo,
"Ochón!" ar siad, "ní sheinnfidh sé port ceoil arís go deo!".

Because of the alacrity with which downstream I shot,
Of the wildlife and the scenery I didn't see a lot.
Past St. Emilion's vineyards I was carried by the flow,
And I tried to do the breast-stroke with a mermaid near Bordeaux.

Leis an sruth do bhíos á scuabadh síos abhainn uasal an Dordogne;
Bhí uisce i mo chluasa, im bhéal is i mo thóin;
Bhíos deimhnitheach go rabhas ar mo shlí go flaithis Dé,
Is bhí scéal mo bháis ar R na G ar nuacht áitiúil a sé.

Céilí House played solemn tunes that night to help the nation grieve,
And they had a minute's silence at a match in Páirc Uí Chaoimh;
The papers all paid tribute and reported my mishap,
And the Times of London said "he was a rather jolly chap".

Dar liom nach raibh aon rogha agam, ach bás a fháil go h-óg,
Go raibh mo chluiche críochnaithe, 's gur séideadh an fheadóg;
Do chuimhníos ar an domhan so, lán d'éagóir agus d'uafás,
Is gur mhór an faoiseamh éirí as, is glacadh leis an mbás.

So to this cruel and unjust world I gladly said goodbye;
To greedy multinationals and politicians sly;
All racist thugs and superpubs and boy-bands you can keep,
As I leave behind this life unkind, and drift into the deep.

Ach tháinig scéal na tubaiste go dtí an dá gharsún,
An fliúiteadóir Mac Bhuilcín is an píobaire De Brún;
Do ghlaodar ar Ó Cearbhaill agus d'inis dó an scéal,
Is bheartaigh siad go gcaithfidís mé tharraingt slán ó bhaol.

So the rescue party bravely dived into the fearsome pond;
They reached the massive estuary the French call La Gironde;
"If we don't find this man tonight" says Browne, "I am afraid,
The sharks will dine on box-player in a red wine marinade".

They swam and searched most thoroughly until the break of day,
They found me drifting hopelessly, afloat in broad Biscay;
They nudged me gently towards the shore, this bold and valiant crew,
Like a team of tugboats trying to dock the noble QE2.

Ar thalamh tirim na Fraince, nuair a thána-sa chugam féin,
Ar mo mhuintir bhí lúcháir nach bhfuaireas bás i bhfad i gcéin.

Dá olcas é an saol, bheadh cúpla bliain agam go fóill,
Is chun beatha a chur thar n-ais sa chorp, seo linn go tigh an óil.

Now I'm safe home, but when I roam to party, pub or rave,
The people boast they've seen a ghost returned from the grave;
They try to hide, or move aside with many a nervous glance,
Saying "Am I mad, or is that the lad who drowned last year in
France?"

Baking Tips

Stories of other people's birthday parties don't usually excite the listener's imagination. Bearing this in mind, the idea that I might make up a song about my fortieth birthday seems far-fetched, but a remarkable example of the art of the patissier was to lead me to a fateful decision.

The reader will have gathered by now that The Four Star Trio have played a huge part in my life over many years: playing with Johnny McCarthy and Pat "Herring" Ahern has been a constant pleasure. Their insistence on high musical standards has been an inspiration, and our sessions have never been solemn or dull. The story of "The Two-Row Cake" has its origins in a Trio session in the Spailpín Fánach bar in Cork's South Main Street one February night. When, as I feared, the lads interrupted the tune in hand to give a rousing blast of "Happy Birthday to You" and the lights were dimmed to draw attention to the blazing candles, I was amazed to see that the cake was shaped like an accordion, complete with two rows of buttons.

This gastronomic delight was the work of Geraldine McCarthy (née Murray), wife of Johnny. Not only was it of striking appearance, but when cut and distributed it proved delicious, and were it not for some photographs taken at the time we might have doubted its existence later, since all traces of it were quickly devoured by the Spailpín's clientele. I thought long and hard about how best to express my appreciation for Ger's heroic culinary feat, and I concluded that a song would be appropriate. This proved a demanding task, and when I had spent some weeks assembling a few lines I lost courage and shelved the project. Several years later I came across the pages again, and had another go, with a different melody in mind. This time I managed a decent few verses, and when I sang them the reaction was favourable. One of the hardest things about writing songs is airing them in public for the first time: however convinced one is of the quality of the work, there is always the fear of failure, of stony silence.

The air of "The Two-Row Cake" is a version of a well-known jig called "Larry O'Gaff", and it was used most famously in a marvellous song called "Paddy's Panacea", also popularly known as "Stick to the Craythur". I remember learning the words of this song after I'd heard Johnny Moynihan singing it some time in the early seventies. The words were written by one Joseph Lund and published in *The Emerald Isle Songbook* (M.H.Gill, Dublin 1899), but it was Tom Lenihan, the great singer from Knockbrack in West Clare, who set them to this tune and who popularised the song by including it in his vast repertoire. In more recent years, Jim McFarland, that fine singer from Derry, married this air to a lovely poem by Brian McGinnis in praise of the Dungiven cobbler, Willie Ward. Jim's version of "Willie Ward" is on his album *A Taste of Tradition: Mountain Streams.*

There must be something about the tune that brings out the positive in us: all three songs are songs of unstinted praise. I am well aware that the air appealed to me because I was thinking along roughly the same lines as the author of "Paddy's Panacea", trying to create a song of praise that would be comical largely because of its exaggerated claims for the substance being extolled. The use of historical and medical allusions was probably inspired unconsciously by the older song too. Predictably, the final verse, with its references to medical and aphrodisiac qualities, usually inspires listeners to ask me for the recipe.

The Two-Row Cake

Come all you young bakers and bold pastry-makers,
Remain wide awake or you'll miss my discourse,
If you have no objections I'll sing of confections,
Of taste and perfection I'll sing till I'm hoarse.
This gem of cuisine from the fair Geraldine,
It appeared on the scene without flaw or mistake;
For nourishment hearty the soul of the party
Was surely McCarthy's accordion-shaped cake.

In a manner bewitching she brought from her kitchen
A cake that was rich in ingredients rare;
There was flour and oatmeal and Chiver's mixed peel,
A pint of tequila and two Spanish pears.
It was iced like a dream with chocolate and cream
In a mixture supreme that was smooth and opaque.
Then with care and with lovin', with heavin' and shovin',
She placed in the oven the double-row cake.

In the course of our tunes in the Spailpín saloon
There were many who swooned when this cake was unveiled;
Their eyes they did doubt and their tongues they hung out,
They abandoned their stout and their eloquence failed.
Gene Rabies the piper, he pounced like a viper,
Big portions he swiped till his belly did ache.
As our glasses we drained till we addled our brains,
With the finest champagne we washed down the sweet cake.

If the great Julius Caesar had this in his freezer,
He'd handle with ease those conspirators sly;
And old Louis Sixteen with his bitch of a queen
Would have dodged guillotines and lived on in Versailles.
The Armada from Spain wouldn't journey in vain,
But would victory gain over Admiral Drake;
'Twould have saved Brian Boru from that Norwegian crew
If he only could chew on the gadget-shaped cake.

This confection so quaint will cure all your complaints,
You'll never feel faint or have trouble with nerves;
Its exquisite flavour will make your heart braver,
Impressing the neighbours with spirit and verve.
This great work of genius will stiffen your penis,
Preventing all heinous hangovers and shakes;
For all pains and infections, unwanted erections,
You'll get full protection from Geraldine's cake.

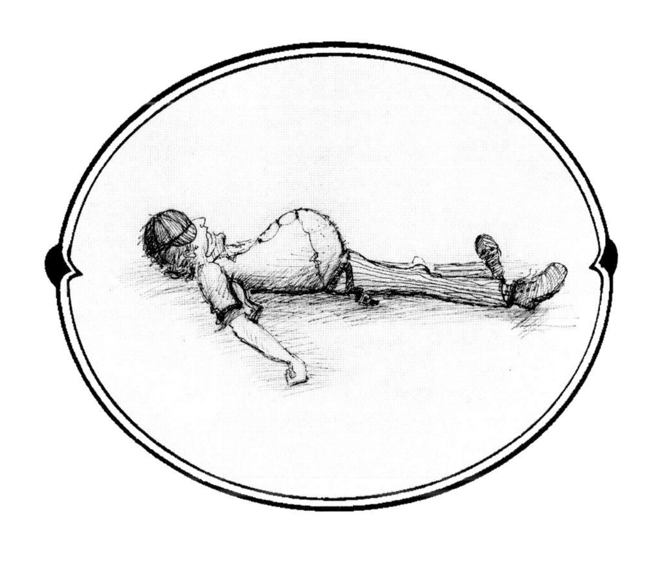

Testing the Water

The Pool Song

I suspect "The Pool Song" was not the first song to be inspired by a pub conversation. In the mid-seventies I made the acquaintance of Jimmy Crowley, who was the first song-writer I had ever met. Throughout my teens I had always been in awe of good song-writers, Lennon and McCartney being the idols at the time, but writing songs was something I never considered an option for myself. The only recently composed traditional-style songs I had heard up to then were the comic songs sung by Cór Chúil Aodha, such as "Scoil Bharr d'Inse", "An Poc ar Buile", and some of the songs of George Curtin and Patsy Cronin.

When the pool craze hit Ireland's pubs, many publicans saw it as an added attraction to alleviate the boredom of the daytime drinker, just as present-day bars offer an endless series of soccer matches on big screens. The table was often given pride of place in the main bar: in later times it was relegated to a back room or custom-built pool room, but in the mid-seventies it was the centre-piece, guaranteed to draw and retain young men whose ten-pence pieces would eventually more than pay for it. For those of us keen on playing music, singing songs or dancing a set, it was a pestilence sent from Hell to try our patience, though some enlightened publicans made their priorities clear by insisting on closing down the pool table as soon as a singer or musician came in. Among that number were Dónall Ó Catháin of Baile an Fhirtéaraigh and Tommy George Breatnach of An Bóthar, both in West Kerry.

These were the very thoughts that formed my conversation with Jimmy Crowley one night in early 1975, and before we parted company Jimmy suggested we give vent to our feelings in a song. I agreed to have a go at the first draft. During the following week I had to attend a very monotonous work-related meeting, and being securely seated in the back corner of the room, I wrote most of the song during the two hours; some of my colleagues must have been deeply impressed by my assiduous note-taking. When I showed the verses to Jimmy the following night in the Phoenix bar, he declared that it was fine, and that he couldn't improve on what I had done. Within a few months, he had recorded it as part of his first album with Stoker's Lodge, *The Boys of Fairhill.* Not only had I written a song, but it had been recorded, in an era when traditional and folk albums were still major events!

The air – and the opening phrase – is that of "The Clonmel Cows", a song I had first heard sung by Paul Frost and subsequently on many occasions by Diarmuidín Ó Súilleabháin, who was working in Cork at the time and who was one of the many fine singers and musicians who frequented the Phoenix. "The Clonmel Cows", a song lamenting the plight of the small farmer, was composed by Frank Cronin from Glenflesk, probably some time in the fifties, to judge by the references to politicians such as Dev and John A. Costello.

Finally, a strange and rather ironic story concerning the fate of this song. Shortly after I had written it I spent a weekend with some friends in Killarney during a Pan-Celtic festival. The Sunday being wet, and no sign being found of a tune or a song, we spent the afternoon in a pub playing pool. When we left, I forgot to bring my jacket, and didn't miss it until we were back in Cork. I was also unaware of the fact that the words of "The Pool Song" were on a few pages in the pocket of the same jacket. During the week the contents of the pocket (including the song) arrived by post. It was only then I realised that this was the only copy of the song in existence, and that I had almost lost it while playing the very game I professed to hate. I never got the opportunity to thank the kind thief who kept the jacket but scrupulously returned its contents.

The Pool Song

May the Lord upon high who rules the sky look down on our pubs and bars;
For the people therein, both women and men, are neglecting their pints and their jars.
The crack it is bad, the atmosphere sad; every man has a face like a mule,
And all they can do is grab an ould cue and start playing that game of pool.

Now when I was a boy 'twas always my joy to visit the pub each night.
There were arguments, scraps, and beatings perhaps, and everyone thought he was right.
There were badgers and dogs and men from the bogs and young fellas acting the fool,
But now there's no crack, for every man jack has his arse in the air playing pool.

To the rural alehouse, after milking the cows, every customer made his way;
And there they would dwell and drink till they fell, while the fiddles and pipes they did play.
The jigs and the reels and the rattling of heels and the polkas and slides were the rule,
But now there's no chance of a tune or a dance, for everyone's playing th'ould pool.

Now this pool you will find is a game designed for foolish illiterate louts;
You puts in four bob and you press an ould knob, and a big shower of balls they come out;
They are placed on a table, and then if you're able, you knock them all into a hole;
Then more money goes in, you start over again, and you lose every bob of your dole.

In the Irish Free State all the people are bate from watching and playing this game.
In their necks they have cricks which no doctor can fix, and their backs and their shoulders are maimed;
Their arses protrude in a manner most lewd, from being hoisted aloft in the air,
And their eyeballs are sore and dripping in gore, and they act in a manner most quare.

So if you meet a young man whose face is wan and whose eyes have a vacant stare;

If his jaw it is slack, and his head is thrown back, and he can't tell a
cob from a mare;
With his head corrugated, his nostrils dilated, his manners like those of
a fool;
Then your shirt you can bet that you have just met a man who's gone
mad for pool.

Courtroom Drama

The Strange Case of the Miltown Fourteen

When in the video shop, I tend to avoid the shelves marked "true story", on the principle that if the story is good and is well told, its veracity is completely irrelevant. I must declare, however, that this song is based on fact, and despite my exaggerations and my customary abuse of poetic licence, even the bare facts (insofar as they can be ascertained through the fog of history, popular lore and sentimental reminiscence) are quite astonishing.

A group of musicians is "found on" in a Miltown Malbay pub in mid-afternoon on a February Sunday: through sheer coincidence (or possibly on the droll whim of some court official) the case is called for the week of the Willie Clancy Summer School, when anyone who knows the accused is aware that they will all be in town; the accused, on arrival, are not allowed enter the courtroom; the case is heard to the sound of Irish traditional music being played in the next room; the solicitor for the accused delivers an impassioned plea which stresses their musical abilities, and the importance of music in the life of the area; and the judge responds by striking out the charges. The acquittal is celebrated with a hearty music session back at the scene of the "crime", where toasts are drunk to the legal eagle who is the hero of the day, and to the fiddle-player whose fortieth birthday was being celebrated at the time of the offence.

This reads like a sub-plot for the remake of *The Quiet Man*, but Tom Queally, the publican in the case, opted for song rather than film, and asked me to commemorate the occasion in verse. The song puts flesh on the bones of the story as outlined above, although it doesn't explain the background music or the failure to admit the accused to their own trial. The court was usually held in the Community Hall in Miltown, but as there were set-dancing classes in progress, our case had to be heard in an office which wasn't big enough to accommodate the fourteen accused: we waited outside, listening to the taped music being blasted at the set-dancers, while our fate was decided in the little office.

As is clear from the song, Henry Benagh, the birthday boy, is a native of Tennessee, a fine fiddle-player who came to Ireland in the late seventies. He now lives in West Clare and runs a restaurant in Ennis. I am assured by those who have heard the song that it will amuse people who don't know Henry or any of the other characters mentioned: local references are a vital part of most comic song-writing, and a well-made song will entertain even those listeners who are unfamiliar with the characters in the story.

This song has developed sad associations for me in recent times, with the news that Queally's pub, one of the great music pubs of West Clare, has closed down. Tom and Baby Queally and their family have always been kind to musicians and have been strong supporters of the Willie Clancy School since its foundation. The pub has suffered the fate of many others in the area, including great music venues such as Hennessy's in Miltown, Conway's in Mullagh and Gleeson's in Coore.

The air of this song is one well known in West Muskerry. George Curtin's "My Pup Came Home from Claodach" is probably the most popular song to use it. Pead Buí Ó Loingsigh also wrote a comic song called "Trucail Pheige Breátha" to this air.

The Miltown Fourteen

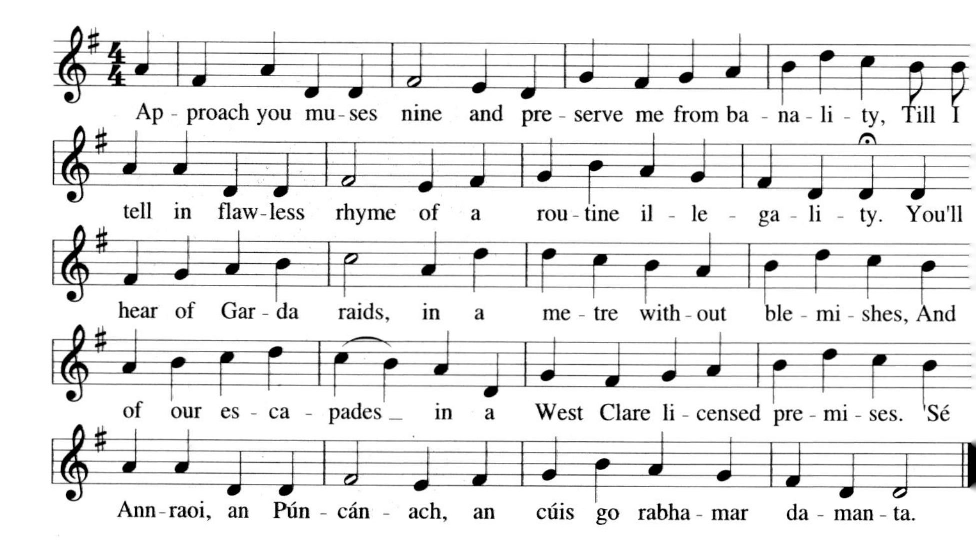

Approach, you Muses nine, and preserve me from banality,
As I sing in flawless rhyme of a routine illegality.
You'll hear of Garda raids in a metre without blemishes,
And of our escapades in a West Clare licensed premises.

Chorus
Is é Annraoi an Poncánach an chúis go rabhamar damanta.

Oh, the birth of Henry Benagh we gathered to commemorate,
Through mist and fog and rain, at his shrine we came to venerate.
There were some came on by train, or by hackney-car professional,
And one came in by plane into Miltown International.

To the house of Friel we motored, where Maurice King was *fear a' tí*,
Dispensing beer and porter, and barking with profanity.
Good friends and kind relations, we spread good will and levity,
Partaking of libations to mark the Yank's nativity.

And some Irish tunes we played with great taste and virtuosity,
Our talent we displayed in those reels of high velocity.
Mick Flynn we then obliged to sing a song that was not very brief,
As we filled our bellies to the brim with porter and with curried beef.

But travel, talk and booze on our stamina was soon to tell,
So we all went for a snooze in the Malbay Luxury Hotel.
Bright Phoebus shone on high as we crept along the passages;
Though feeling far from spry, we attacked the eggs and sausages.

By feeble health undaunted, we marched abroad to Spanish Point,
And for Sunday lunch we sauntered into Tom Queally's drinking joint.
There were some who couldn't face it, quite overcome by fear and
doubt,
But once they got to taste it, they were throwing themselves at pints of
stout.

So we gladly wet our mouths with Tom Queally's patent remedies;
Then the instruments came out and we played more Gaelic melodies.
Our thoughts were not of crime, but of pleasure and frivolity,
We cared not for the time, nor for legal technicalities.

But paid spies and informers have oft betrayed the Gael before,
So without a previous warning, the Guards paraded in the door.
Our music then was spoiled, and a doleful silence took its place,
Tom dropped his barman's smile and put on his undertaker's face.

May the devil take that Judas who to the lawmen offered us,
May the worms gnaw his tubes, his intestines and oesophagus.
In hell he'll roast and bake, full of drought and frequent nausea,
While we above partake of celestial ambrosia.

The sergeant nearly cried, saying "This music is so beautiful,
It breaks my heart inside, but I fear I must be dutiful".
Then he wrote down all our names in a manner most meticulous,
Though him we did not blame, but an Irish law ridiculous.

So the fateful day arrived when we faced the rigours of the law,
And this historic trial did great media attention draw.
The lawyers in Miltown Courthouse wore ermine gowns and wigs of
wool,
And Muiris, to support us, put on a special summer school.

The prosecuting counsel demanded savage punishment,
He said we were low scoundrels, deserving death or banishment.
If he sat in the judge's seat, from Co. Clare he'd have us banned,
He'd amputate our hands and feet and transport us to Van Diemen's
Land.

In the course of this oration, we stood together in the dock,
With fear and trepidation our piss flowed down into our socks.
Up rose our liberator, Loughnane, employed to plead our cause,
A courtroom gladiator, quite expert in our Irish laws.

Says he, "It is outrageous, in Willie Clancy's native place,
That history's storied pages should tell a tale of such disgrace.
To think these fine performers, all virtuosos in their prime,
By traitors and informers stand accused of perfidy and crime".

So spoke our man with feeling, as to the charges he replied,
To the learned judge appealing, while hardened adults sobbed and
cried.
He spoke of Henry Benagh and his fiddle-playing ability,
And how his friends all came to see him moving towards senility.

Then the judge he cleared his throat, and the crowded public gallery
Of friends and loyal supporters were quiet as monks in Melleray.
Says he, "These men accused are a special case with little doubt,
They are no common boozers, no Wolfe Tones fans or lager louts".

"But the music of our nation in hands like these won't fade or sink,
So I'll put you on probation, you're free to go and have a drink.
Our music to support, and this triumph to commemorate,
All future sessions of this court I hereby ban and terminate".

As we shouted and rejoiced that our sentence could have been so soft,
Tom Queally we did hoist shoulder-high and carried him aloft.
At the invitation of our host we drank black beer and Hennessy,
And we raised our glasses in a toast to the rambling boy from
Tennessee.

The Animal Kingdom

The air of "The Seanbhean Bhocht" has been used for generations in Cúil Aodha and Baile Mhúirne for light-hearted songs that lampoon some local character, or record some comical event in the area. One such song is "Frank Kelly's Tree", which tells how Jer Leary got hurt cutting a tree for Proinsias Ó Ceallaigh and claimed compensation. A more caustic use of the tune is the late Deaglán Tallon's "The Cruiser", a satire on Conor Cruise O'Brien, written when O'Brien was a government minister in the seventies, with additional lines to mark his appointment as Editor-in-Chief of *The Observer*. The air has been used for countless other songs, many of which were intended as passing comments on topical events that are long since forgotten.

I wrote "The Kerry Animals" in February of 2004, some weeks after Páidí Ó Sé, then manager of Kerry's football team, had been quoted in the media as likening his county's supporters to "rough fucking animals". The remark, made during a team holiday in South Africa, would have been laughed off, and appreciated as a tribute to the demanding character of Kerry football people, were it not for the presence of reporters, who duly conveyed it onto the pages of their papers. Coming as it did during the post-Christmas season when sports stories are scarce, it, and the reactions it provoked, filled many a column inch for weeks.

I was booked to perform as featured singer in the Cork Singers' Club weekly session shortly after the "animals" furore. Someone suggested that I should make a song about the Kerry story, and I thought it would be nice to have something new to sing in the Club, so I had a go. This, I decided, will be a bit of fun, to be sung once and promptly forgotten. As often happens in such cases, people kept demanding the song over the subsequent weeks, and it also went down well when I sang it later that month in Skibbereen. All sports followers know the law which states that rivalries between counties, towns or parishes become more heated as you move closer to the boundary between the two sides.

I have yet to sing the song in Kerry, although I'm told that Páidí himself is keen to hear it. Like so many Cork people, I have great affection for Kerry (despite what their footballers often do to us), and I owe a lot to Kerry people. I spent most of my spare time in my late teens and my twenties in the Gaeltacht area of Corca Dhuibhne and made many friends there. Since taking up traditional music I, along with many of my colleagues, have a special interest in the music of Sliabh Luachra, and my debt to the musicians of that area is incalculable. Kerry has been a considerable element in my education, musical and linguistic. This song, therefore, was conceived as a gentle, affectionate reaction to what was clearly a clumsy throwaway remark.

The Kerry Animals

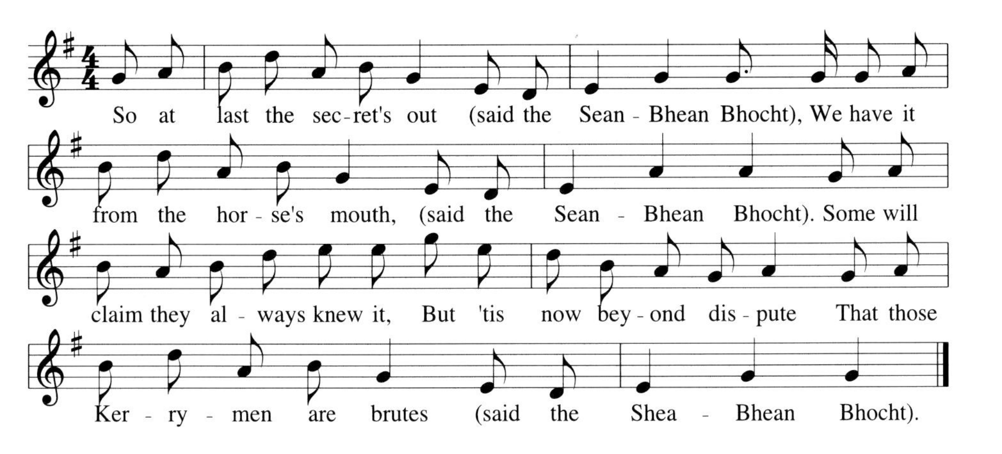

So at last the secret's out (said the Sean-bhean Bhocht)
We have it from the horse's mouth (says the Sean-bhean Bhocht):
    Some will claim they always knew it,
    But 'tis now beyond dispute
That those Kerrymen are brutes (says the Sean-bhean Bhocht).

For the signs were always there . . .
Like Healy-Rae's distinctive hair . . .
    And they have this strange mystique,
    With their footballing technique,
And that funny way they speak . . .

I don't wish to make a fuss . . .
But they're clearly not like us . . .
    In that kingdom so remote
    Every August, you will note,
For their king they crown a goat . . .

On safari we will go . . .
From Banna Strand to Templenoe . . .
    'Twill be just like Noah's Ark

Where things bleat and growl and bark,
All in Páidí's Wildlife Park . . .

And we'll study Kerry's beasts . . .
Both the living and deceased . . .
'Twill be dangerous enough
And conditions will be tough;
Páidí said they can be rough . . .

Castleisland's chimpanzees . . .
Ballyheigue's performing fleas . . .
With Kilgarvan's kangaroos
And the Kenmare cockatoos,
Plus Killarney's Kerry Blues . . .

In Ard an Bhóthair things are slack . . .
But we'll get the tourists back . . .
There'll be zoologists *go leor*
Going on field trips by the score,
All flying into Farranfore . . .

But if you think I am too bold . . .
With those lads in green and gold . . .
Don't neglect to have your say,
Send your message off today;
All complaints to P. Ó Sé . . .

PÁIDÍ'S WILDLIFE PARK
CIARRAÍ

Our Own Saint

Like many Irish saints, St. Finbarr seems to be a blend of fact and myth, of Christian and pagan character, and I'm not sure if he is formally acknowledged on the Vatican's official list. To Cork people he is a name taken for granted, cropping up everywhere: there must have been many Corkonians who were born in St. Finbarr's Hospital, christened in a church that bears his name, educated in one of his schools, engaged in sporting activities with his hurling and football club or his athletic club, had financial dealings with a credit union called after him, lived in a street named for him, and are now lying peacefully in St. Finbarr's Cemetery.

Certainly there can be very few people in Cork who haven't had dealings with his name at some time in their lives.

In spite of the ubiquitous nature of the man, there are remarkably few folk-tales in popular currency, and few, if any, songs about him: no equivalent of "St. Patrick Was a Gentleman", and no hymn to rival the popularity of "Dóchas Linn Naomh Pádraig" or "Hail Glorious St. Patrick". As you may have gathered, "A Hymn to St. Finbarr" had its origins in a shamrock-wetting session one March in the late seventies, when some cranky, chauvinistic (in other words, typical) Corkman complained that Our Own Man was getting no glory at all compared to that feckin' blow-in who has us all marching and drinking every 17th of March. My memories of this conversation are vague, but I'm certain that at some point I must have pointed out that St. Finbarr's Day is the 25th of September, and that the only institution that ever took a day off to celebrate was my alma mater, St. Finbarr's College, Farranferris.

So when I set about writing the song, it was clear to me that Finbarr had to be portrayed as the ultimate Corkman, an exaggerated version of our own self-image, with a little touch, perhaps, of the outsider's impression of the Corkonian. Having lived all of my working life in the city, but being a native of the Skibbereen area, I was probably as well qualified as anyone else to balance the insider's view with this independent impression. After depicting the obvious sporting and poteen-making scenes, I recalled that the traditional, Civil Service view of Corkonians was that they bought a one-way ticket to Dublin and, shortly after their arrival, grabbed all the top jobs (to which we would naturally reply that de cream comes to de top, boy). Therefore Finbarr's elevation to the Papacy was the logical climax to the song. I also remembered one of Niall Tóibín's great lines, in a comedy routine where he described the sentimental renderings of "De Banks" and "Dear Old City by the Lee" at closing time in a Leeside bar: he claimed that the Corkman is the only one who can feel homesick while he is at home. Thus, our hero refuses to accept the prospect of exile to a strange Italian city where there's no chance of a floury spud, and as for a decent pint of Beamish or Murphy . . .

The air is that of a slip jig called "Moll Roe" which is also used in a song called "Táim in Arréars", popular in Cúil Aodha and Baile Mhúirne.

A Hymn to St. Finbarr

You may talk of the saints and the scholars
Whose names we all learned in school,
Who found Europe in sin and in squalor
And brought it to order and rule.
A fig for these globe-trotting clerics,
St. Ronan, St. Brendan, St. Gall;
The man who gave women hysterics
Was Finbarr so handsome and tall.

Chorus
You can keep St. George and his dragons,
St. Pat with his shamrocks and snakes,
For drinking the quarts and the naggins
St. Finbarr the trophy must take.

While others were off gallivanting
In Brussels, Berlin and Paree,
Finbarr his vespers was chanting
At home in his church by the Lee.
His miracles all were astounding
But surely, of all his great work,
His finest achievement was founding
The beautiful city of Cork.

St. Canice above in Kilkenny
At hurling had made quite a name;
He suffered an awful shock when he
Took on our Finbarr at the game.
St. Finbarr he hurled like lightning
By pulling first time, low and high:
He gave the poor man such a frightening
He thought that the doomsday was nigh.

At bowling he cut quite a figure
On tarmac or gravel or sods;
Men who were many times bigger
He beat by incredible odds.

At drag-hunts and racetracks and meetings
His dogs always won with a will,
And ever since then there's no beating
The dogs of the boys of Fairhill.

Incensed at the heavy taxation
On brandy and spirits and wine,
Finbarr gave his dispensation
To all, without penance or fine.
So the hills of West Cork were infested
With men making poteen and rum,
Which then they consumed and digested
To make themselves totally numb.

Bould Finbarr, being always ambitious
And eager to taste a *smeathán*,
In a way that was most surreptitious
He founded a still in Guagán.
The stuff that he made was delicious
And eagerly sought and imbibed,
But delivered an impact so vicious
That no one who drank it survived.

At a conclave inside in St. Peter's
The cardinals said with one voice,
As they quaffed the red wine by the litre,
That Finbarr for Pope was their choice.
On hearing that he was elected
And urgently summoned to Rome,
St. Finbarr the job he rejected,
Remarking "Dere's no place like home".

St. Finbarrs
Hooch

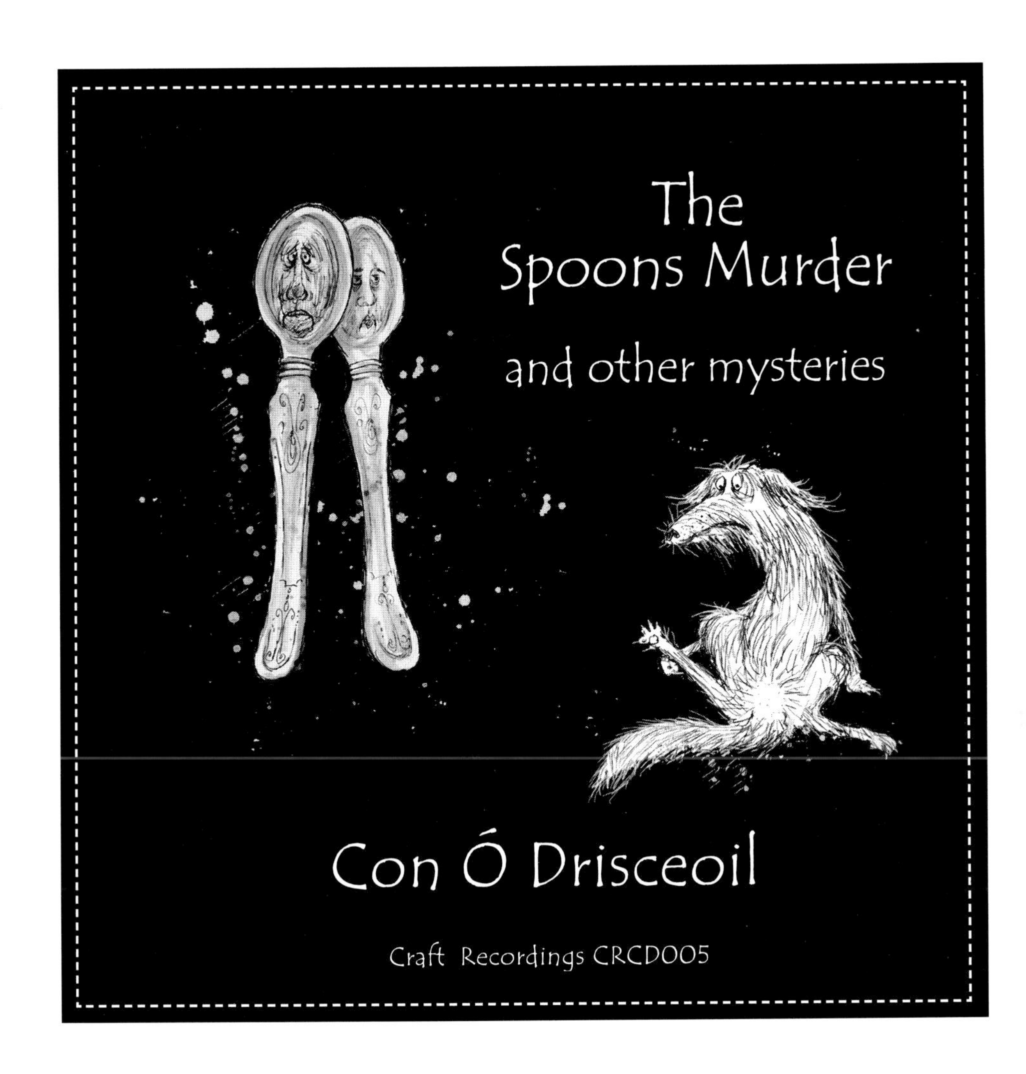

Cut along the dotted lines above to obtain an insert suitable for using with a CD jewel case.

The Spoons Murder and other mysteries

Con Ó Drisceoil

1 : Bob's Song
2 : The Milltown Cockroach
3 : The Spoons Murder
4 : Ben Hur
5 : The Irish Piper
6 : King Lear
7 : Sink or Swim
8 : The Two-Row Cake
9 : The Pool Song
10 : The Miltown Fourteen
11 : The Kerry Animals
12 : A Hymn to St. Finbarr

All songs composed and arranged and sung by Con Ó Drisceoil, except: "Ben Hur": composed C.O.D., arranged by C.O.D. and Pat Ahern, featuring Pat Ahern on octave mandolin and guitar, and "A Hymn to St. Finbarr": composed C.O.D., arranged C.O.D., Pat Ahern and Johnny McCarthy; featuring Johnny McCarthy on fiddle, whistle and vocals, Pat Ahern on guitar, and Con Ó Drisceoil on vocals, harmonium and organ.
All tracks recorded at Clonmoyle East, Co. Cork 2005-2006.
Engineered, produced and mastered by Pat "Herring" Ahern.
Except Track 12: recorded and mixed at Secret Garden Studios, Cork 1997; produced by Terry Moylan, Jerry O'Reillyl and The Four Star Trio; engineered by Johnny Campbell, assisted by Rupert MacCarthy-Morrogh.

Con Ó Drisceoil - The Spoons Murder & other mysteries CRAFT CRCD005

The Spoons Murder

and other mysteries

Con Ó Drisceoil

1 : Bob's Song (2:45)
2 : The Miltown Cockroach (4:02)
3 : The Spoons Murder (5:11)
4 : Ben Hur (7:19)
5 : The Irish Piper (3:58)
6 : King Ler (4:60)
7 : Sink or Swim (4:59)
8 : The Two-Row Cake (2:41)
9 : The Pool Song (2:54)
10 : The Miltown Fourteen (9:07)
11 : The Kerry Animals (2:45)
12 : A Hymn to St. Finbarr (4:31)

CRCD005 - Craft Recordings, 71 Bluebell Road, Dublin 12. Tel: 086-8507572

Con Ó Drisceoil - The Spoons Murder & other mysteries CRAFT CRCD005

Cut along the dotted lines above to obtain an insert suitable for using with a CD jewel case.

Con Ó Drisceoil - The Spoons Murders & other mysteries CRAFT CRCD005